THE INTERNATIONAL RESCUE BOOK OF

THUNDERBIRDS

FAB CROSS-SECTIONS

THE HOOD'S SUBMARINE - TECHNICAL DATA

1. Missile storage bay, 2. Missile launchers, 3. Port navigation light. 4. Control room, 5. Emergency exit to airlock, 6. Topside airlock, 7. Sleeping bunks and chemical toilet, 8. Access ladder to engine monitoring room, 9. Access ladder to airlock, 10. Maintenance hatch to turbines, 11. Port drive turbine, 12. Atomic generator, 13. Ballast/flotation tanks, 14. Auxiliary booster turbines.

RAVETTE BOOKS

The technical details of Thunderbirds featured in
this book were drawn and compiled by
Graham Bleathman

CONTENTS

© 1993 ITC Entertainment Group Ltd
Licensed by Copyright Promotions Ltd

Edited and compiled by Alan Fennell
Artwork by Graham Bleathman

First Published by Ravette Books Limited 1993

Printed and bound for Ravette Books Limited
8 Clifford Street, London W1X 1RB
An Egmont Company
by Proost International Bookproduction, Belgium

ISBN 1 85304 362 1

THIS IS Tracy Island

To the outside world, Tracy Island is one of several atolls owned by multi-millionaire industrialist and space shuttle manufacturer Jeff Tracy.

Jeff Tracy's two man jet is used primarily for collecting supplies: at speeds in excess of 2000mph, the Australian mainland is less than half an hour away.

Tracy House. A large two storey building in which Jeff lives with his family, Kyrano and Tin Tin. Brains, the young scientist who designed the Thunderbird craft also has quarters in the house.

As well as his private aircraft, Jeff Tracy owns a number of boats, including small yachts and motor launches. Also docked at the island is Lucille, a luxury cruiser named after Jeff's late wife.

Left: The Cliff House overlooks the island's runway and jetty beyond, while the Round House (below) is used primarily for guests if all the rooms at the main house are full. They conceal hangars to Thunderbird 2 and 3 respectively.

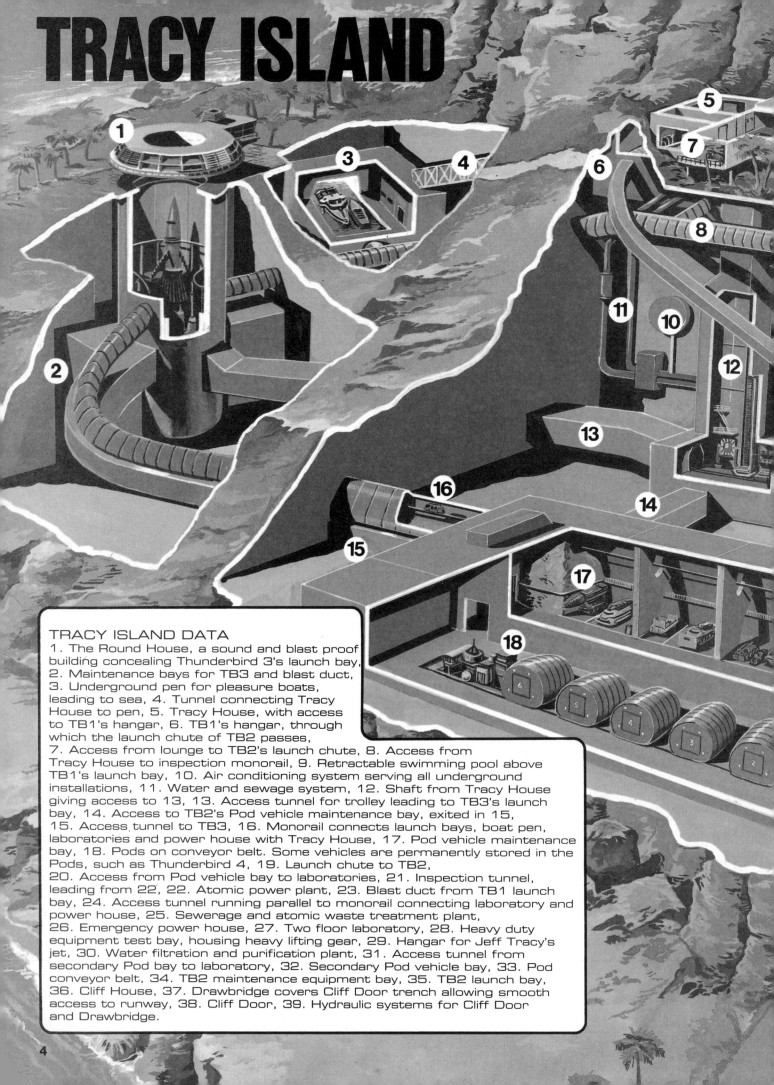

TRACY ISLAND

TRACY ISLAND DATA

1. The Round House, a sound and blast proof building concealing Thunderbird 3's launch bay, 2. Maintenance bays for TB3 and blast duct, 3. Underground pen for pleasure boats, leading to sea, 4. Tunnel connecting Tracy House to pen, 5. Tracy House, with access to TB1's hangar, 6. TB1's hangar, through which the launch chute of TB2 passes, 7. Access from lounge to TB2's launch chute, 8. Access from Tracy House to inspection monorail, 9. Retractable swimming pool above TB1's launch bay, 10. Air conditioning system serving all underground installations, 11. Water and sewage system, 12. Shaft from Tracy House giving access to 13, 13. Access tunnel for trolley leading to TB3's launch bay, 14. Access to TB2's Pod vehicle maintenance bay, exited in 15, 15. Access tunnel to TB3, 16. Monorail connects launch bays, boat pen, laboratories and power house with Tracy House, 17. Pod vehicle maintenance bay, 18. Pods on conveyor belt. Some vehicles are permanently stored in the Pods, such as Thunderbird 4, 19. Launch chute to TB2, 20. Access from Pod vehicle bay to laboratories, 21. Inspection tunnel, leading from 22, 22. Atomic power plant, 23. Blast duct from TB1 launch bay, 24. Access tunnel running parallel to monorail connecting laboratory and power house, 25. Sewerage and atomic waste treatment plant, 26. Emergency power house, 27. Two floor laboratory, 28. Heavy duty equipment test bay, housing heavy lifting gear, 29. Hangar for Jeff Tracy's jet, 30. Water filtration and purification plant, 31. Access tunnel from secondary Pod bay to laboratory, 32. Secondary Pod vehicle bay, 33. Pod conveyor belt, 34. TB2 maintenance equipment bay, 35. TB2 launch bay, 36. Cliff House, 37. Drawbridge covers Cliff Door trench allowing smooth access to runway, 38. Cliff Door, 39. Hydraulic systems for Cliff Door and Drawbridge.

THUNDERBIRD 1
TECHNICAL DATA

GrahamBleathman91

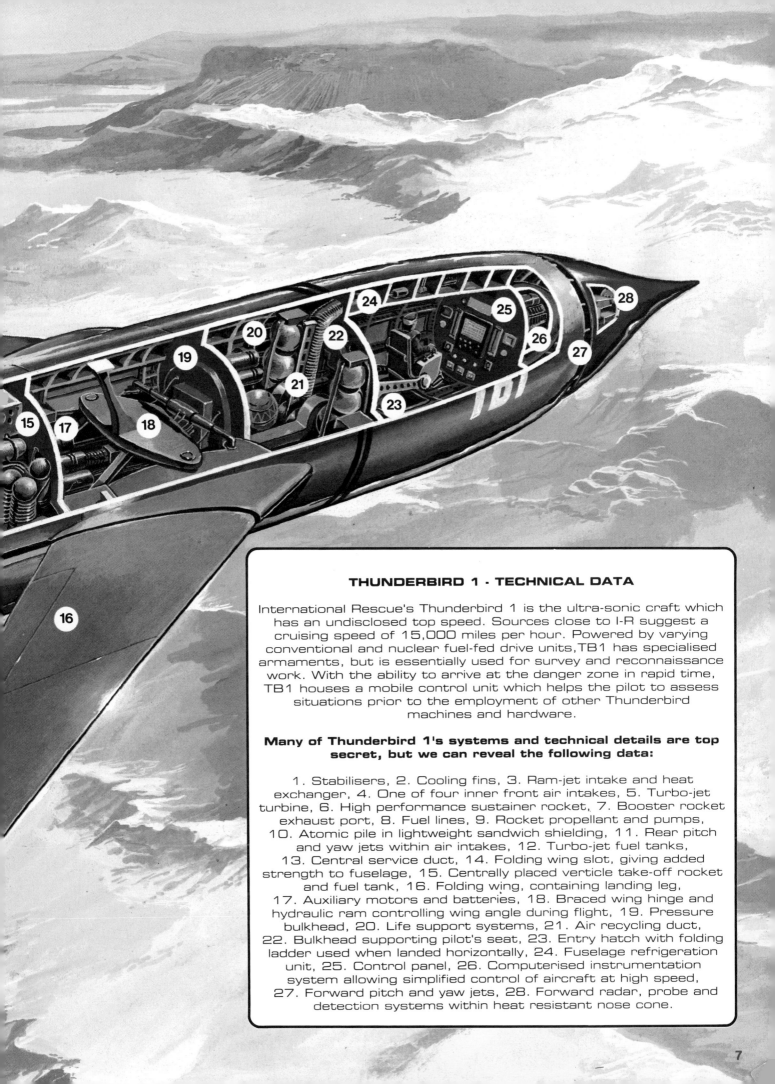

THUNDERBIRD 1 · TECHNICAL DATA

International Rescue's Thunderbird 1 is the ultra-sonic craft which has an undisclosed top speed. Sources close to I-R suggest a cruising speed of 15,000 miles per hour. Powered by varying conventional and nuclear fuel-fed drive units, TB1 has specialised armaments, but is essentially used for survey and reconnaissance work. With the ability to arrive at the danger zone in rapid time, TB1 houses a mobile control unit which helps the pilot to assess situations prior to the employment of other Thunderbird machines and hardware.

Many of Thunderbird 1's systems and technical details are top secret, but we can reveal the following data:

1. Stabilisers, 2. Cooling fins, 3. Ram-jet intake and heat exchanger, 4. One of four inner front air intakes, 5. Turbo-jet turbine, 6. High performance sustainer rocket, 7. Booster rocket exhaust port, 8. Fuel lines, 9. Rocket propellant and pumps, 10. Atomic pile in lightweight sandwich shielding, 11. Rear pitch and yaw jets within air intakes, 12. Turbo-jet fuel tanks, 13. Central service duct, 14. Folding wing slot, giving added strength to fuselage, 15. Centrally placed verticle take-off rocket and fuel tank, 16. Folding wing, containing landing leg, 17. Auxiliary motors and batteries, 18. Braced wing hinge and hydraulic ram controlling wing angle during flight, 19. Pressure bulkhead, 20. Life support systems, 21. Air recycling duct, 22. Bulkhead supporting pilot's seat, 23. Entry hatch with folding ladder used when landed horizontally, 24. Fuselage refrigeration unit, 25. Control panel, 26. Computerised instrumentation system allowing simplified control of aircraft at high speed, 27. Forward pitch and yaw jets, 28. Forward radar, probe and detection systems within heat resistant nose cone.

THUNDERBIRD 2
TECHNICAL DATA

Fantastic in its power and strength, Thunderbird 2 is constructed of an alloy developed by Hiram Heckenbacker, fondly known to the International Rescue team as "Brains". With interchangeable Pods, Thunderbird 2 carries vital heavy engineering and life saving equipment at speed to the danger zone. An estimated cruising speed of 2000 m.p.h. has been recorded and optimum altitude for TB2 is 60,000 feet, but as with other International Rescue craft and systems, much of the technical data is secret. We are however, able to reveal the following details:

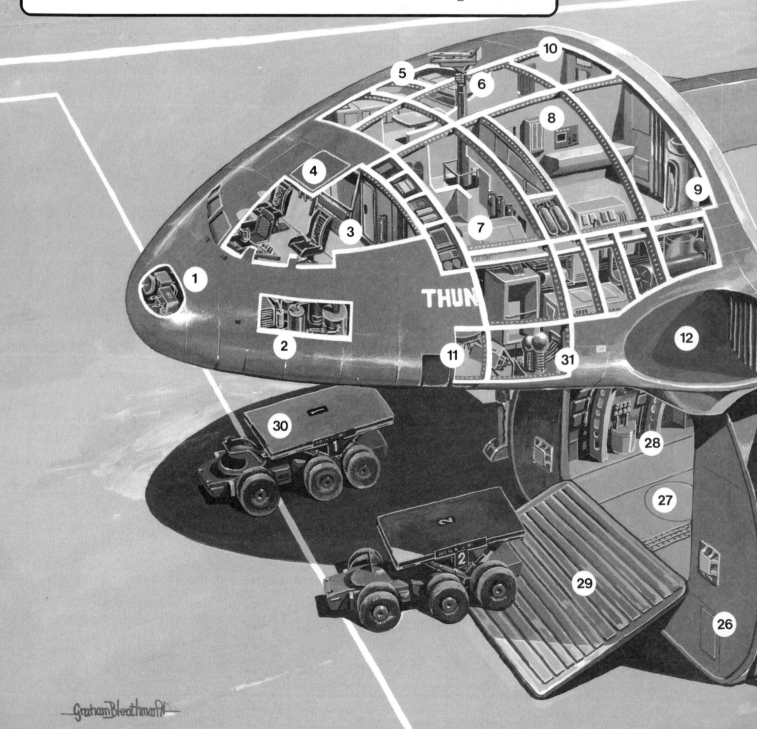

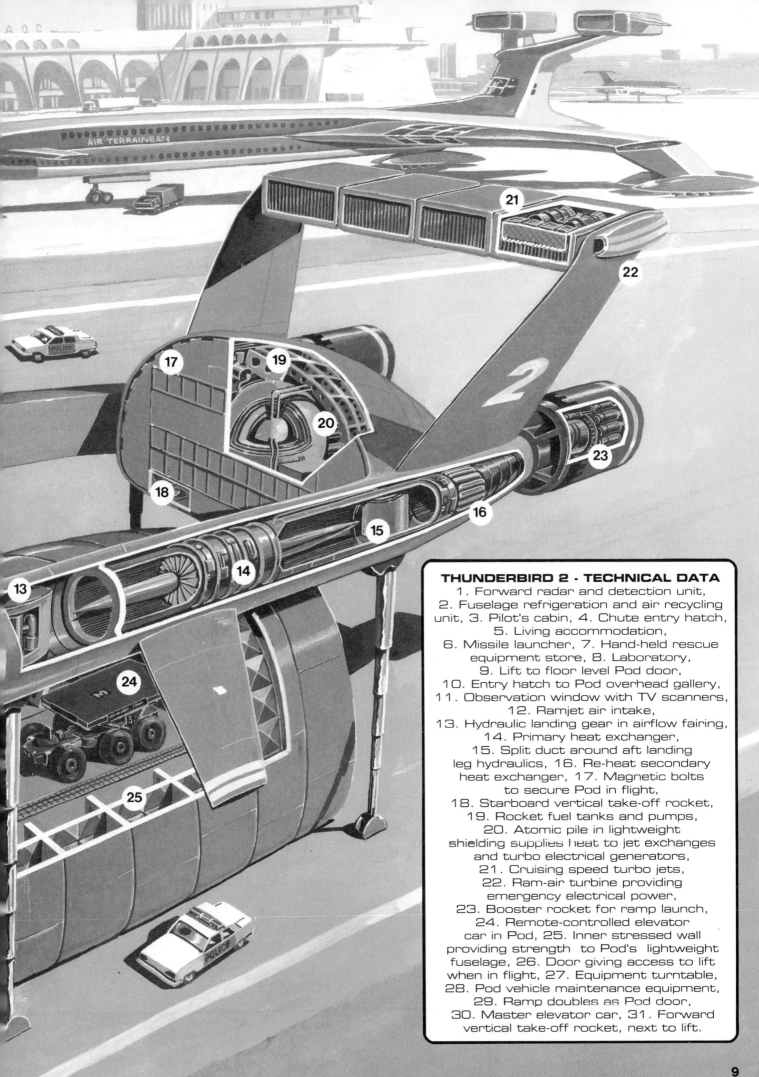

THUNDERBIRD 2 · TECHNICAL DATA

1. Forward radar and detection unit,
2. Fuselage refrigeration and air recycling unit, 3. Pilot's cabin, 4. Chute entry hatch,
5. Living accommodation,
6. Missile launcher, 7. Hand-held rescue equipment store, 8. Laboratory,
9. Lift to floor level Pod door,
10. Entry hatch to Pod overhead gallery,
11. Observation window with TV scanners,
12. Ramjet air intake,
13. Hydraulic landing gear in airflow fairing,
14. Primary heat exchanger,
15. Split duct around aft landing leg hydraulics, 16. Re-heat secondary heat exchanger, 17. Magnetic bolts to secure Pod in flight,
18. Starboard vertical take-off rocket,
19. Rocket fuel tanks and pumps,
20. Atomic pile in lightweight shielding supplies heat to jet exchanges and turbo electrical generators,
21. Cruising speed turbo jets,
22. Ram-air turbine providing emergency electrical power,
23. Booster rocket for ramp launch,
24. Remote-controlled elevator car in Pod, 25. Inner stressed wall providing strength to Pod's lightweight fuselage, 26. Door giving access to lift when in flight, 27. Equipment turntable,
28. Pod vehicle maintenance equipment,
29. Ramp doubles as Pod door,
30. Master elevator car, 31. Forward vertical take-off rocket, next to lift.

SPECIFICATIONS OF THUNDERBIRD 3

A staggering 200 feet in length, Thunderbird 3 is piloted by Alan Tracy. Scott, and sometimes Brains and Tin Tin, usually accompanies Alan on space missions. Apart from space rescue work, the orange spaceship is also used for the regular servicing of Thunderbird 5 and as a shuttle for the transfer of personnel as Alan and brother John take it in turns to man the International Rescue earth-orbit satellite.

GrahamBleathman91

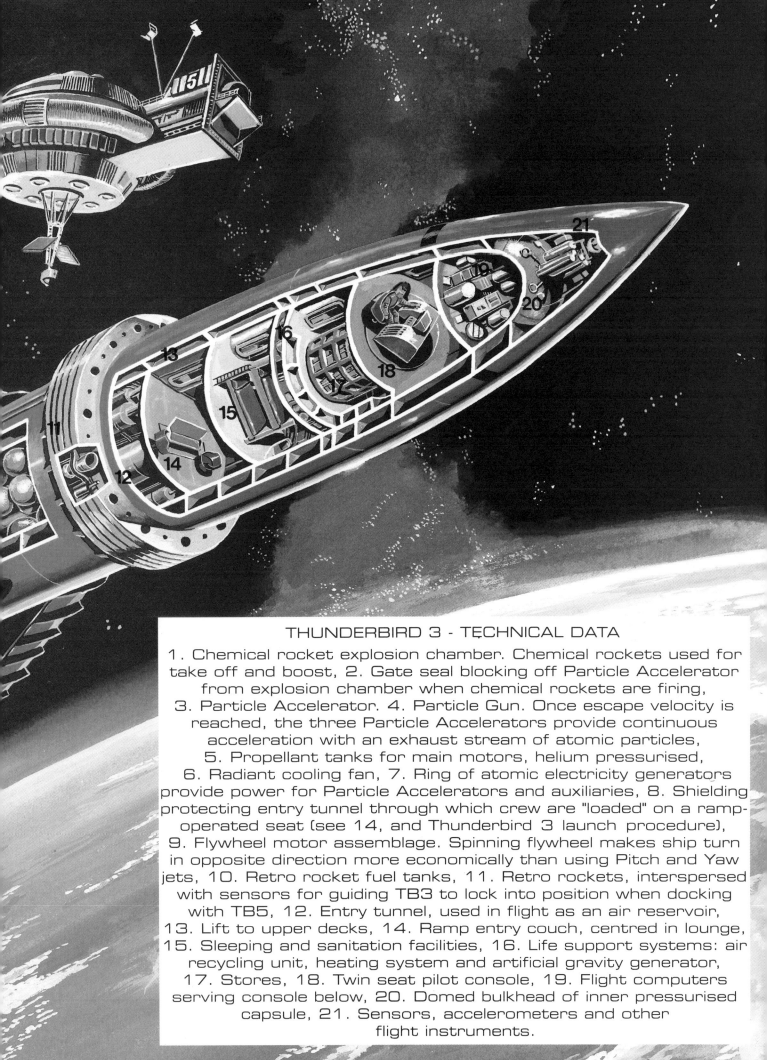

THUNDERBIRD 3 - TECHNICAL DATA

1. Chemical rocket explosion chamber. Chemical rockets used for take off and boost, 2. Gate seal blocking off Particle Accelerator from explosion chamber when chemical rockets are firing, 3. Particle Accelerator. 4. Particle Gun. Once escape velocity is reached, the three Particle Accelerators provide continuous acceleration with an exhaust stream of atomic particles, 5. Propellant tanks for main motors, helium pressurised, 6. Radiant cooling fan, 7. Ring of atomic electricity generators provide power for Particle Accelerators and auxiliaries, 8. Shielding protecting entry tunnel through which crew are "loaded" on a ramp-operated seat (see 14, and Thunderbird 3 launch procedure), 9. Flywheel motor assemblage. Spinning flywheel makes ship turn in opposite direction more economically than using Pitch and Yaw jets, 10. Retro rocket fuel tanks, 11. Retro rockets, interspersed with sensors for guiding TB3 to lock into position when docking with TB5, 12. Entry tunnel, used in flight as an air reservoir, 13. Lift to upper decks, 14. Ramp entry couch, centred in lounge, 15. Sleeping and sanitation facilities, 16. Life support systems: air recycling unit, heating system and artificial gravity generator, 17. Stores, 18. Twin seat pilot console, 19. Flight computers serving console below, 20. Domed bulkhead of inner pressurised capsule, 21. Sensors, accelerometers and other flight instruments.

SPECIFICATIONS OF THUNDERBIRD 4

Small by comparison to the rest of the Thunderbird craft, and of considerably shorter range, Thunderbird 4 is nonetheless a vital member of the International Rescue team.

This one-man submarine carries in its nose tubes an array of specialised equipment - including laser cutters, rams and missiles to clear obstacles - to deal with every underwater emergency. Transported to the danger zone in Thunderbird 2, TB4 is manned by experienced aquanaut Gordon Tracy.

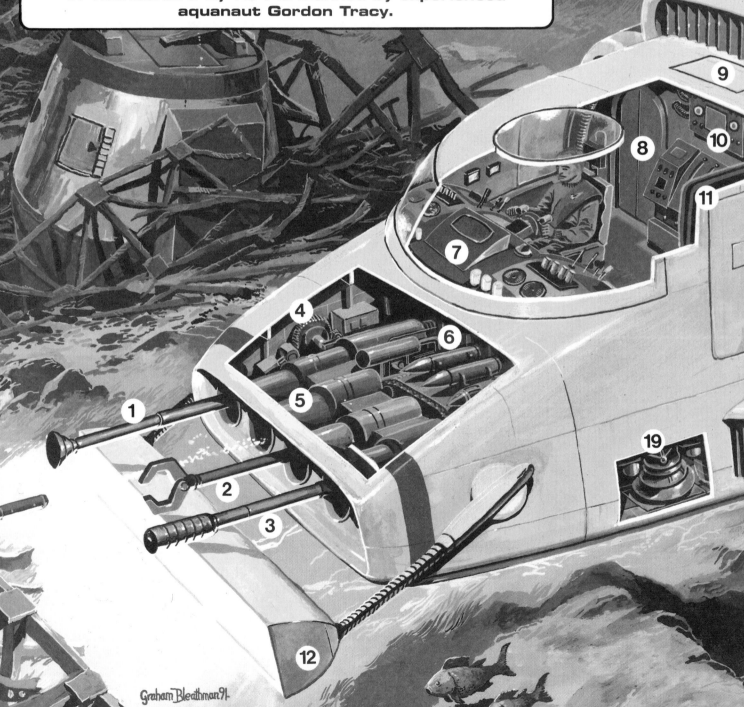

Graham Bleathman 91

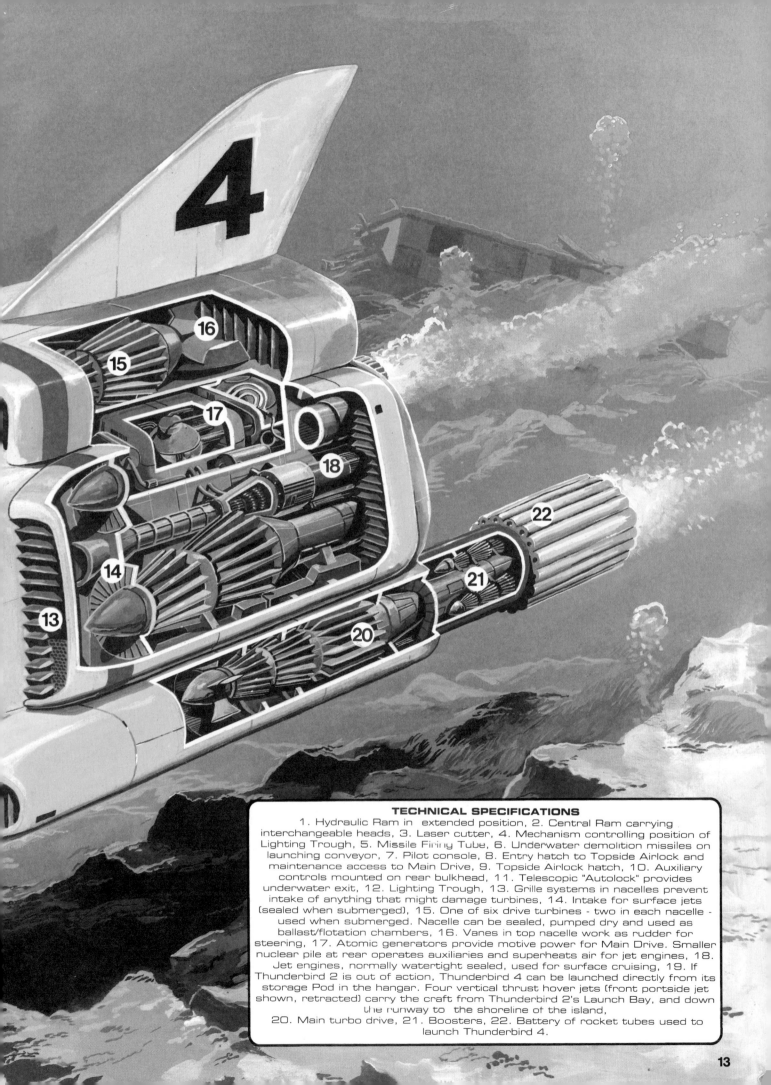

TECHNICAL SPECIFICATIONS

1. Hydraulic Ram in extended position, 2. Central Ram carrying interchangeable heads, 3. Laser cutter, 4. Mechanism controlling position of Lighting Trough, 5. Missile Firing Tube, 6. Underwater demolition missiles on launching conveyor, 7. Pilot console, 8. Entry hatch to Topside Airlock and maintenance access to Main Drive, 9. Topside Airlock hatch, 10. Auxiliary controls mounted on rear bulkhead, 11. Telescopic "Autolock" provides underwater exit, 12. Lighting Trough, 13. Grille systems in nacelles prevent intake of anything that might damage turbines, 14. Intake for surface jets (sealed when submerged), 15. One of six drive turbines - two in each nacelle - used when submerged. Nacelle can be sealed, pumped dry and used as ballast/flotation chambers, 16. Vanes in top nacelle work as rudder for steering, 17. Atomic generators provide motive power for Main Drive. Smaller nuclear pile at rear operates auxiliaries and superheats air for jet engines, 18. Jet engines, normally watertight sealed, used for surface cruising, 19. If Thunderbird 2 is out of action, Thunderbird 4 can be launched directly from its storage Pod in the hangar. Four vertical thrust hover jets (front portside jet shown, retracted) carry the craft from Thunderbird 2's Launch Bay, and down the runway to the shoreline of the island,
20. Main turbo drive, 21. Boosters, 22. Battery of rocket tubes used to launch Thunderbird 4.

SPECIFICATIONS OF
THUNDERBIRD 5

In a secret orbit around the Earth hangs Thunderbird 5, vital communications satellite of International Rescue. TB5 is constantly manned by either John or Alan Tracy, and monitors communications world-wide to give instant warning of potentially dangerous events.
I-R's "ear in space" also picks up radio transmissions on all wavebands and frequencies selecting special reference to rescue and emergency situations.
Supplies for the satellite are provided by Thunderbird 3 which docks with TB5 at regular intervals to facilitate maintenance and shift change-overs.

Graham Bleathman 91.

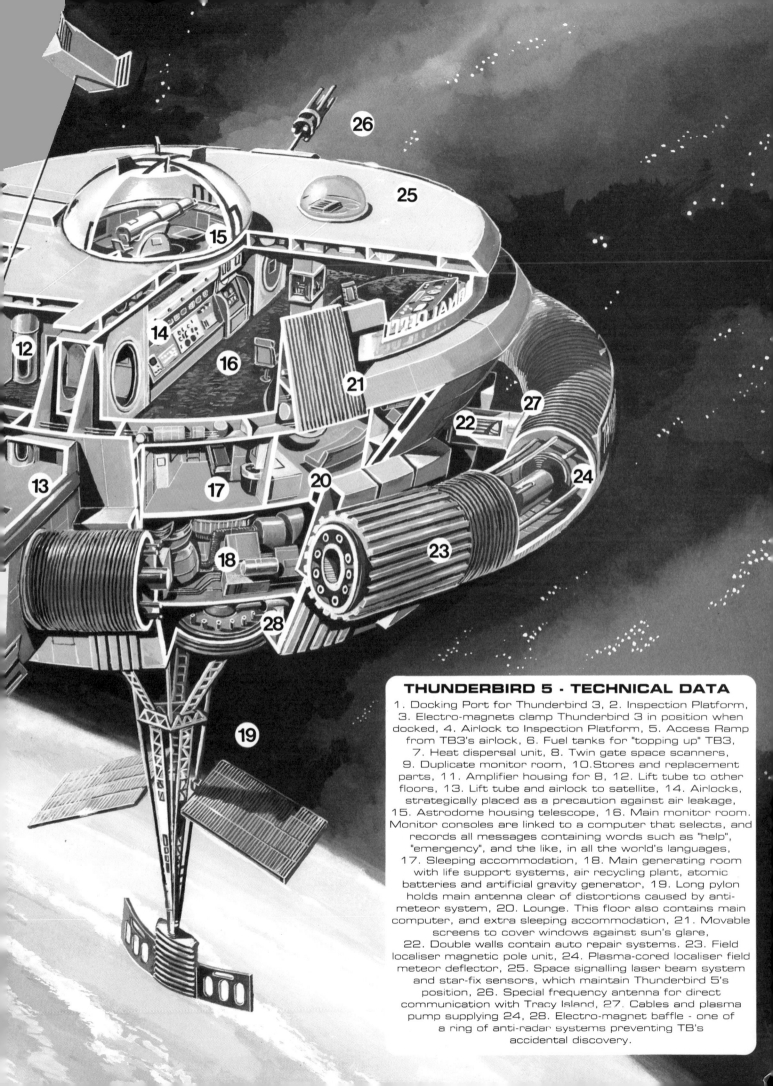

THUNDERBIRD 5 · TECHNICAL DATA

1. Docking Port for Thunderbird 3, 2. Inspection Platform, 3. Electro-magnets clamp Thunderbird 3 in position when docked, 4. Airlock to Inspection Platform, 5. Access Ramp from TB3's airlock, 6. Fuel tanks for "topping up" TB3, 7. Heat dispersal unit, 8. Twin gate space scanners, 9. Duplicate monitor room, 10. Stores and replacement parts, 11. Amplifier housing for 8, 12. Lift tube to other floors, 13. Lift tube and airlock to satellite, 14. Airlocks, strategically placed as a precaution against air leakage, 15. Astrodome housing telescope, 16. Main monitor room. Monitor consoles are linked to a computer that selects, and records all messages containing words such as "help", "emergency", and the like, in all the world's languages, 17. Sleeping accommodation, 18. Main generating room with life support systems, air recycling plant, atomic batteries and artificial gravity generator, 19. Long pylon holds main antenna clear of distortions caused by anti-meteor system, 20. Lounge. This floor also contains main computer, and extra sleeping accommodation, 21. Movable screens to cover windows against sun's glare, 22. Double walls contain auto repair systems. 23. Field localiser magnetic pole unit, 24. Plasma-cored localiser field meteor deflector, 25. Space signalling laser beam system and star-fix sensors, which maintain Thunderbird 5's position, 26. Special frequency antenna for direct communication with Tracy Island, 27. Cables and plasma pump supplying 24, 28. Electro-magnet baffle - one of a ring of anti-radar systems preventing TB's accidental discovery.

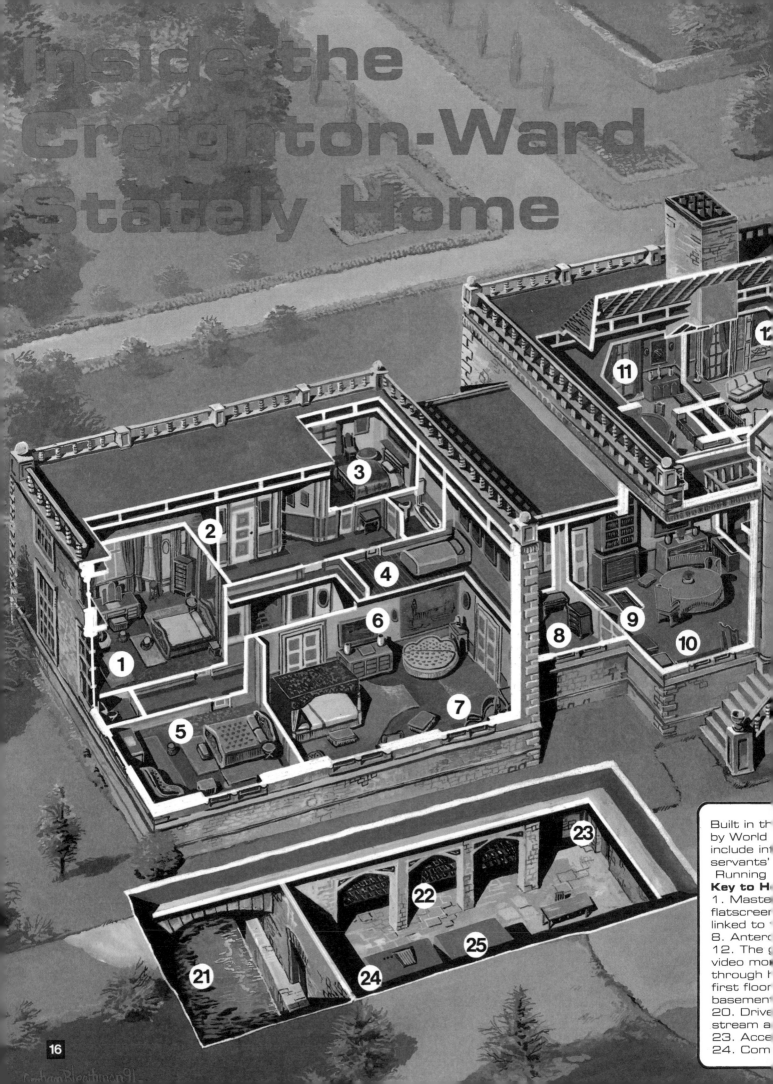

Inside the Creighton-Ward Stately Home

Built in th
by World
include in
servants'
  Running
Key to H
1. Maste
flatscreen
linked to
8. Antero
12. The g
video mo
through h
first floor
basement
20. Drive
stream a
23. Acce
24. Com

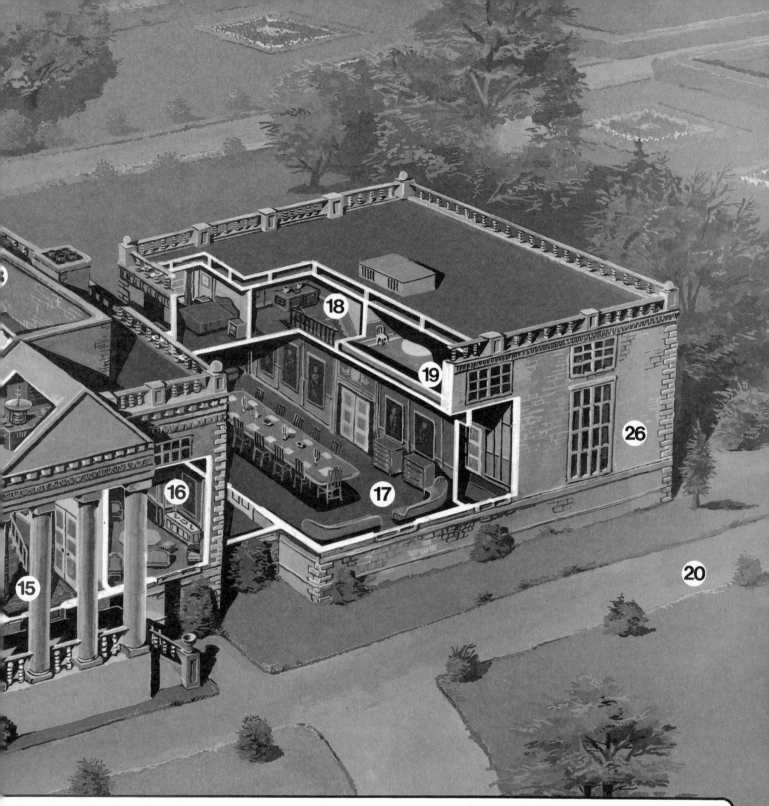

...nteenth century, the Creighton-Ward Mansion stands on the site of a Norman castle in rural Kent. Designated ...as a grade one listed building, Creighton House has nonetheless been extensively, yet subtly, modernised to ...rglar alarms, inter-room video communications, and a forensic laboratory has been built in what were the ...t quarters "below stairs".

...kept to a minimum: only Parker and Lil the cook live permanently on site with her ladyship.

...ures:

...m, 2. First floor guest rooms, 3. Parker's bedroom, 4. Guest bedrooms, 5. King Charles bedchamber, 6. LCD ... TV monitor: all rooms are linked via disguised video screens behind paintings. Hidden anti-intruder cameras ...ed burglar alarm system also transmit pictures to any designated monitor, 7. Lady Penelope's bedroom, ...rary, 9. Under-floor safe hidden under carpet, designed by Parker and Brains, 10. Library, 11. Games room, ...wing room, 13. Attic containing emergency power system, 14. Satellite communications system links mansion ...em with Thunderbird 5. Audio messages to hidden radio receivers (such as her ladyship's teapot) also boosted ...g with TV transmissions from around the world, 15. Hall and entrance behind portico, containing staircase to ...ns, 16. Reception hall, 17. Banquetting hall, 18. Stairs to first floor rooms. Below these are stairs to the ...servants' quarters, including Lil's kitchen, 19. Recreation room, including art studio, book and video library, ...g to FAB 1's garage and visitors' centre for tourists, both adjacent to the east wing, 21. Underground ...eads from ornamental lake via the basement to sluice gates at the river in Creighton Village, 22. Wine cellar, ...vants' quarters (now a forensic laboratory), heating and self contained power system, and Lil's kitchen beyond, ... Weapons store, 26. Ballroom.

Braman was initially invented by Brains as little more than a "toy" something to tinker with in his rare moments of relaxation. It was also designed to provide the brilliant young scientist with a suitable partner for playing chess.

The Tracy boys had provided little challenge in this respect and even Tin Tin's sharp brain was not equal to such a task. So Brains came to the conclusion that if he wanted a chess partner on his level, he'd have to invent one.

Braman also provides an excellent "test bed" for practical application of Brains' theories of mechanics and computer technology.

However, the success of Braman's role (despite it being accidental) in the "Operation Sun Probe" rescue, has led Brains to consider other uses for Braman in International Rescue's work. For example, in a rescue environment where a human being could not possibly survive. To this end he is constantly improving and amending his robot creation.

TECHNICAL DATA

(Illustration shows a recently modified version of Braman)

1. Telescopic computer interface probe (shown extended). Enables Braman to access directly outside computer systems, 2. Articulated pincers - capable of surprising dexterity and delicacy of control, 3. Telescopic hand extension unit (shown extended). Can stretch to a maximum distance of one metre,

4. Remote control radio wave receiver,

5. Lighting units (X 2), 6. Sensory interpretation and relay unit - Braman's "brain", 7. Audio sensors - capable of "hearing" a wide range of sound and vibration frequencies,

8. Electronic eye - capable of reading infra-red and ultra-violet spectra video images seen by eye which can be relayed direct to mobile control or Tracy Island via TB5, 9. Voice box generator and speaker, 10. Neck joint - head can turn 360 degrees and is capable of limited hydraulic extension (maximum 1.3 metres),

11. Release bolts to remove head and collar section, 12. Main frame computer linked directly to "brain", 13. Left arm servo motor and ball/socket joint. Capable of lifting 20 tonnes, 14. Atomic power generator,

15. Emergency back up mini generator,

16. Left arm telescopic mechanism,

17. Telescopic laser cutter (shown extended),

18. Left leg servo motor and ball/socket joint, 19. Back view: Power recharge sockets (X 2), 20. Back view: Power pack activation unit - touch sensitive. Removal of power pack shuts down all Braman's operating systems. 21. Storage hatch for rescue supplies (right leg only shown) - contains first aid kit, mini-breathing equipment etc,

22. Hydraulic knee extension mechanism (inset: shown extended). Maximum extension: one metre, 23. Outer casing - made of cahelium extract X, a super-strong, heat resistant alloy, 24. Auxiliary storage compartments (one on each leg) containing tools, 25. Electromagnetic sole mechanism.

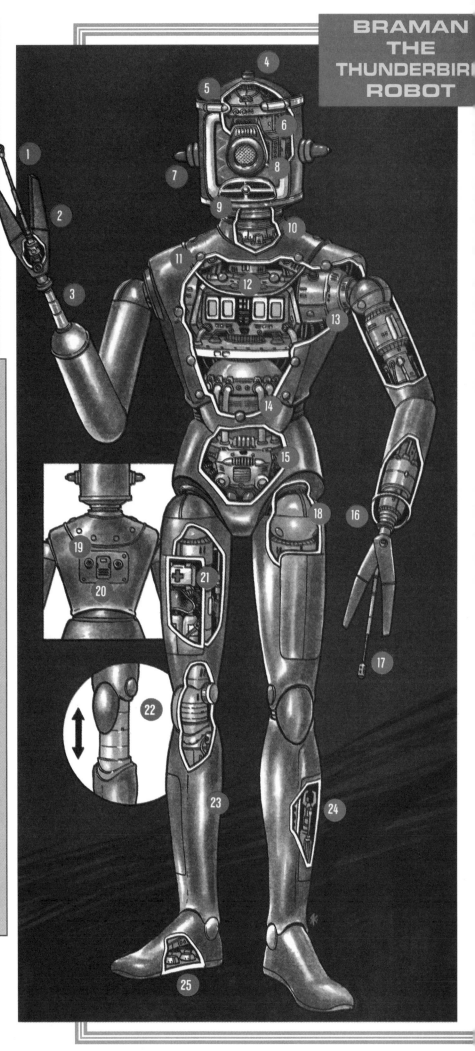

SPOTLIGHT ON
The Pod Vehicles

With new machines constantly under development, the Pod Vehicles are designed to cope with almost any situation. The vehicles are stored either in Thunderbird 2's Pods, or in bays adjacent to TB2's hangar, where they can be more easily maintained. Pictured here are four of the principal vehicles, with the Mole shown in cutaway on the next pages.

The Domo, or Demolition and Object Moving Operator, is capable of lifting or supporting any object up to 50 tonnes in weight, using the three artificial gravity generation suction cups on its arms.

The Firefly is a fire-fighting machine constructed of Cahelium Extract X, one of the toughest metals known. It can travel to the heart of a blaze and snuff out a fire using nitro-glycerine shells fired from its forward gun.

Adapted for rescue, the commercially available truck is called the Jodrell 6, and is designed to aid spacecraft in distress using its long range tractor beam, enabling International Rescue to land ships safely.

Using similar principles to the Domo, the Recovery Vehicles can pull objects up to 500 tonnes if all three vehicles are used simultaneously. Two of these vehicles can be remotely controlled from the third.

THE MOLE - SPECIFICATIONS

TECHNICAL DATA

1. Acoustic Detector and Thermal Imaging System used to detect buried victims, 2. Annular Bearing Rings,
3. Gearing system within Drive Sprocket Ring turns Drill "Bit", 4. Drive Sprocket Ring, powered by: 5. Electric Motor, which in turn is powered by: 6. Shielded Nuclear Reactor, providing direct electric current, 7. Computer and Emergency Control System, 8. Main control system doubles as Mobile Rescue Unit and life support gauges, infra-red and video viewer, Thermal Imaging monitor and steering controls for both Mole and its Trolley, 9. Bench seating (can fold down to provide space for stretchers), 10. Rescue equipment and topside entry hatch,
11. Corridor next to main drive leading to rear emergency exit, 12. Main drive powered by nuclear reactor, with retracted thrust unit. At the start of drilling operations, the unit extends through aft hatch to provide extra downward thrust, 13. Air recycling plant, 14. Port entry hatch, incorporating fold-down ladder, 15, Caterpillar track motor leading to: 16. Gearing system for: 17. Portside caterpillar sprocket drive, 18. Air intakes and filters through bottom of craft, 19. Hydraulic lift system tilts top section of Trolley to desired drilling angle, 20. Liquid oxygen tanks providing emergency propellant for Trolley's engine, 21. 1000 b.h.p high compression engine uses rocket propellant with air as an oxydant, or liquid oxygen if air is absent in rescue location, 22. Wide angle TV camera enables driver to position Trolley before drilling commences, 23. Demolition rocket launcher, 24. Air intake for engine set in rear of Trolley, 25. Hydraulic suspension and brake/clutch gearing system.

SPECIFICATIONS OF
THE FIREFLY

Brains has designed many fire fighting machines for International Rescue. The most successful is the Firefly which incorporates the use of Cahelium Extract X in its construction, one of the toughest metals known. The Firefly can travel to the heart of a blaze and snuff out a fire at its source. This is achieved by firing Nitro-Glycerine Shells through the forward gun mounted behind the Protective Shield.

Graham Bleathman

1. Heat Resistant Shield constructed of Cahelium Extract X. 2. Cahelium - strengthened quartz window. 3. Nitro-glycerine gun. 4. Fume Extractor. 5. Smoke vent. 6. Loading arm holding shell in line with open breech. 7. Hydraulic Recoil Gun mountings. 8. Shell Conveyor from magazine. 9. Headlight. 10. Air filter and Intake. 11. Driver's cabin. 12. Warning Klaxon. 13. Starboard viewpoint and Exit. 14. Remote controlled Searchlight. 15. 800 B.H.P. Power plant drives tracks and main pump through the Power Take Off. 16. Blender Valve from main fuel tank. 17. Main pump. 18. Power Take Off. 19. Gearing, Track Brake and Clutch to Main Drive Sprocket. 20. Hydraulic Suspension. 21. Water Pump. 22. Water Hose Nozzle Supplied through Hose Reel from Pump. 23. Hose Gantry lifts to direct nozzle through 120 degrees for high pressure jet work. 24. Foam Monitor Nozzle.

THE HOOD'S TEMPLE

BASED ON WORLD POLICE FILE AF~GB/92~2

THE HOOD'S TEMPLE

In every nation, across every ocean, the Hood is known Enemy No.1. The whereabouts of his base was unknown recent discovery by operatives of the Universal Secret S and the World Police. The Temple, located deep in the M jungle is believed to be several hundred years old, thoug evident that the Hood has had part of it extended to incl control centre and living accommodation, whilst below vast laboratories and hangars have been built to accomm Hood's array of vehicles. It is believed that these were constructed by a variety of companies owned or run by the many criminal organisations under the Hood's contr

TECHNICAL DATA
1. Concealed hangar for vertical take-off aircraft, connected to the underground garages in the Temple's basement, 2. Anti-radar system preventing accidental discovery of the Temple when the Hood's aircraft take off or land, 3. Main entrance, 4. Entrance hall, protected by heat and pressure sensors, and gas ducts in the walls, 5. Interrogation room, 6. Prisoner cells, 7. Main corridor, protected by video cameras and infra-red detection systems, 8. Bedroom, featuring TV and video system monitoring the interior of the Temple, along with TV broadcasts and worldwide video communications, 9.Communications beacon hidden within pagoda, featuring built in anti-trace system, video/audio communications scrambler, linked directly to control room and video monitors around the Temple, 10. Computerised dressing room containing costumes, disguises and theatrical make up facilities, 11. Kitchen: featuring deepfreeze/microwave oven which stores and prepares the Hood's bulk stores of food, including octopus and squid goulash, peppered mussels, hot liver sandwiches and prune pudding, 12. Guest bedroom, 13. Storeroom, 14. Inner sanctum, 15. Kyrano's statue: around which are curtains, concealed lights and gas burners controlled by computer systems responding to the Hood's voice commands,16. Trophy room, containing loot from past escapades,17. Automated command centre, where computers maintain security of the Temple and monitor world communications for news of International Rescue. 18. Turbo lift to basement level, 19. Garage, featuring a selection of vehicles including the submarine truck, 20. Access tunnel for vehicles to concealed entrance near a remote jungle track five miles away, 21. Atomic power plant, 22. Water purification and filtration system leading to nearby river outlet, 23. Sewerage purification and disposal plant, 24. Blast tunnel from main hangar, 25. Gymnasium, 26. Laboratory and vehicle maintenance area, 27. Weaponry storage room, 28.Main aircraft hangar, 29. Blast duct for aircraft exhaust, 30. Aircraft turntable, 31. One of several stolen World Army Airforce aircraft for use on long distance missions, 32. Anti-aircraft missile defence system, 33. Hangar tunnel, leading to concealed and protected entrance in the jungle two miles away.

MOVING THE EMPIRE STATE BUILDING

1. Built in 1931, the Empire State Building was the world's tallest structure until the World Trade Centre exceeded its 1472 feet height in 1977. It is constructed of sandstone and granite, and has 102 floors, with observation terraces on the 86th and 102nd.
2. Built specially by Universal engineering Incorporated, the power unit is operated under remote control from the nearby site control building.
3. Inspection area monitoring the four building support stanchions.
4. One of the four building support stanchions, designed to maintain the Empire State in an upright position in transit.
5. Internal support structure strengthens the base of the tower during lifting and moving operations.
6. New foundations replaces the original and incorporates a heavy duty track and trolley to move the building.
7. Hydraulic jacks - one of four - that, in conjunction with the now dismantled lift gantry, raise the building's basement floors up to ground level.
8. Power system operates track installation under the building and provides power for the transit trolley.
9. Exit from underground work-site. 10. Atomic power plant for hydraulic jacks.
11. Atomic reactor powers turbines in the power unit. 12. Starboard air intake cools reactor and turbines. 13. Main cahelium-strengthened wheeled drive unit.
14. Starboard turbine. 15. Airbrake and emergency air cooling system.
16. Emergency manual on-board control room.
17. Workforce recreation and eating area.
18. Gray-Houseman road laying vehicle: one of several used to provide temporary roads around the work-site.
19. Site control: Moving operations are conducted from here.
20. Nine-tier observation building: a temporary structure incorporating reception areas for project sponsors and seating for 1000 people, and erected to coincide with the Empire State's final move to its new site.

GrahamBleathman92

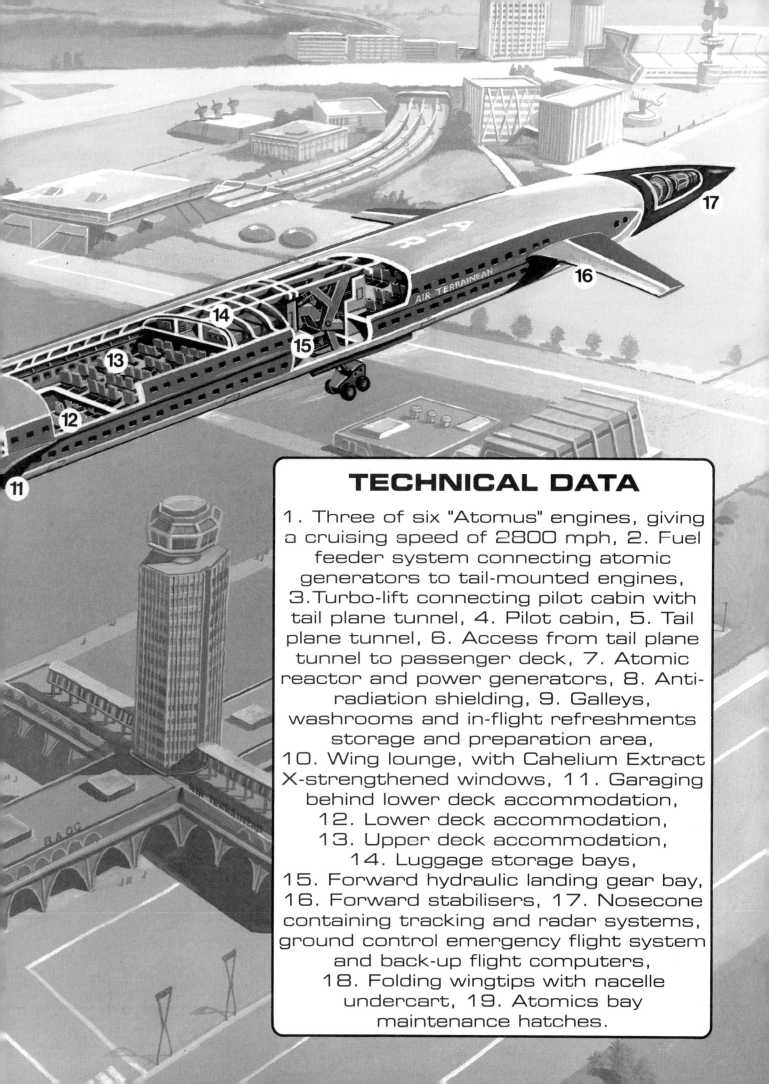

TECHNICAL DATA

1. Three of six "Atomus" engines, giving a cruising speed of 2800 mph, 2. Fuel feeder system connecting atomic generators to tail-mounted engines, 3. Turbo-lift connecting pilot cabin with tail plane tunnel, 4. Pilot cabin, 5. Tail plane tunnel, 6. Access from tail plane tunnel to passenger deck, 7. Atomic reactor and power generators, 8. Anti-radiation shielding, 9. Galleys, washrooms and in-flight refreshments storage and preparation area, 10. Wing lounge, with Cahelium Extract X-strengthened windows, 11. Garaging behind lower deck accommodation, 12. Lower deck accommodation, 13. Upper deck accommodation, 14. Luggage storage bays, 15. Forward hydraulic landing gear bay, 16. Forward stabilisers, 17. Nosecone containing tracking and radar systems, ground control emergency flight system and back-up flight computers, 18. Folding wingtips with nacelle undercart, 19. Atomics bay maintenance hatches.

SPECIFICATIONS OF
FAB 2

FAB 2 is one of several ocean-going pleasure cruisers owned by Lady Penelope. Docked at a secret location on England's south coast, the ship was specially built for her ladyship by International Engineering, a company owned by Jeff Tracy. FAB 2 is capable of attaining a top speed of 100 knots, and can stay at sea without maintenance for three years. It can be operated by one person, or completely automatically using a computerised Auto-bosun.

TECHNICAL DATA

1.Satellite communications room, linking FAB 2 with International Rescue, the Creighton-Ward mansion and monitoring world TV and radio broadcasts,2. One of five lifeboats. A guest bedroom is located behind the two aft port and starboard lifeboats,3. Starboard air vent for upper decks,4. Radar system, 5.Captain's cabin and ship's main computer, 6. Searchlight, 7. Control room, featuring Automatic Bosun, 8.Foghorn, 9.Forward lounge, 10. Lady Penelope's suite, 11. Bathroom, 12.Dining area,13. Bomb-proof garage containing FAB 1, with exit hatches on both sides of the ship, 14. Workshop, with access to the garage, 15.Toilets, 16.Parker's bedroom (Lil's bedroom is on the portside, on the other side of the ship's central corridor,17.Crews' quarters: although the ship can be operated by one person, on-board social functions often require the hire of extra staff. A wardroom is located opposite the crews' quarters on the portside of the ship. 18.Galley, with access to central corridor linking all rooms on this deck, 19. Food hatch for dining area above, 20.Lift to dining room, 21.Starboard winch system leading to main anchor winch located immediately below the forward sun deck, 22.One of several air vents, 23. Laundry room, 24. Stair access to sun deck, 25.Water filtration, purification and sanitation plant, 26.Starboard aquajet, 27. Main turbine, 28.Atomic plant supplying power to turbine and aquajets, 29. Maintenance access to engine room, 30.Engine monitoring room, 31.Armament store and torpedo loading system, 32.Starboard torpedo tubes, 33.Sonar system, 34.Waste filter from sanitation plant.

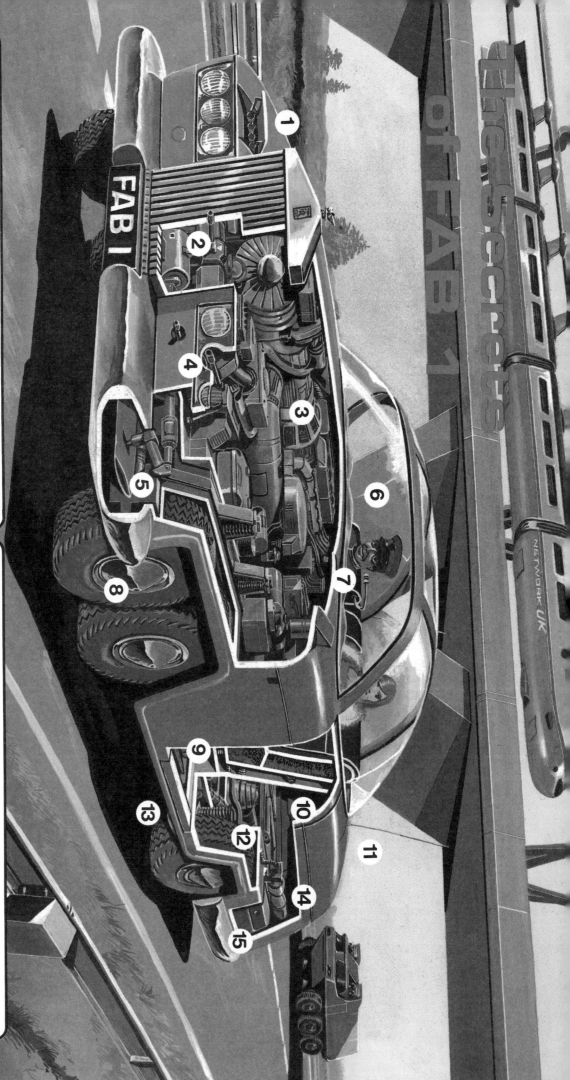

Built under licence from the Rolls-Royce company for the Creighton-Ward family, FAB 1 underwent several modifications when Lady Penelope took possession. These included the incorporation of hydrofoils for travel on water, machine and laser guns, and engine improvements giving a top speed well in excess of 200 mph. Alterations also carried out by International Rescue include a satellite communications system which allows her ladyship to contact Tracy Island via Thunderbird 5 space station at all times.

FAB 1 TECHNICAL DATA

1. Emergency retro air brakes. 2. Primary forward machine gun operated through grille. 3. Rolls Royce engine modified by International Rescue. 4. Secondary machine guns and laser cannons. 5. Adjustable forward hydrofoils extend below wheel level lifting car clear of water. 6. Laminated bullet-proof glass/steel canopy incorporates gull wing split doors. 7. Central driving position includes communications console and controls for machine, laser and harpoon guns. 8. All six wheels incorporate retractable tyre-slashers and studs for snow conditions. 9. Underfloor space for down-and-under doors. 10. Boot space, above hydraulic platform with fold-down safety rails. 11. Satellite, UHF TV and neutronic radio antenna. 12. Rear machine gun and harpoon system propulsion. 14. Smoke and oil dispenser used if FAB 1 is pursued. 13. Rear hydrofoil incorporates a vortex aquajet power unit for water 15. Fuel tanks.